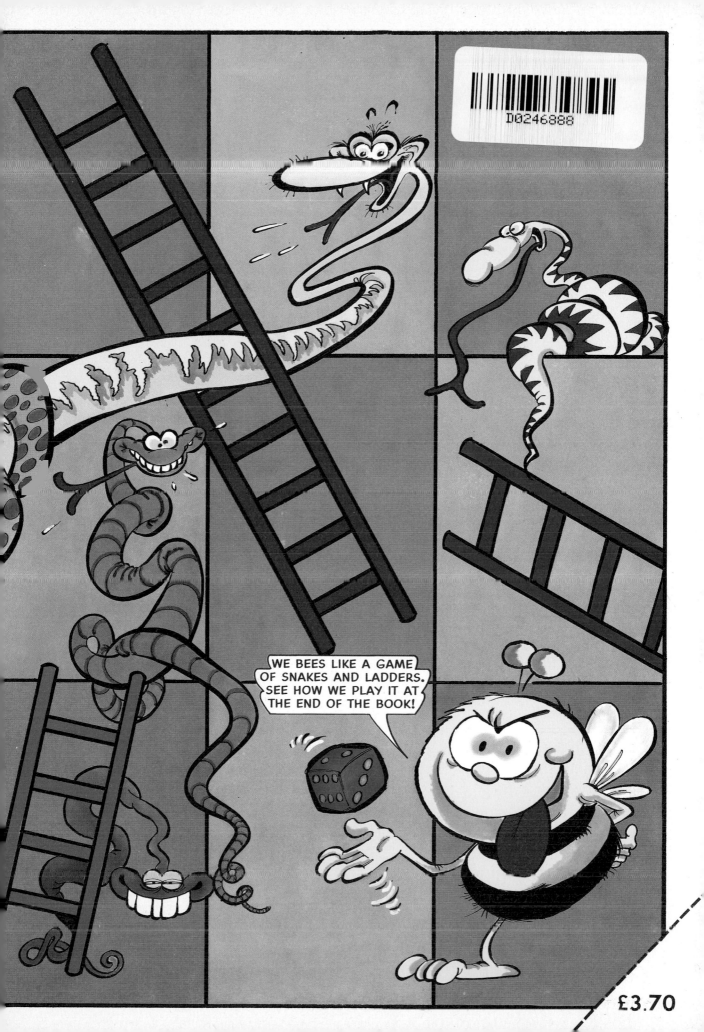

£3.70

Printed and Published in Great Britain by D. C. THOMSON & CO., LTD.,
185 Fleet Street, London EC4A 2HS.

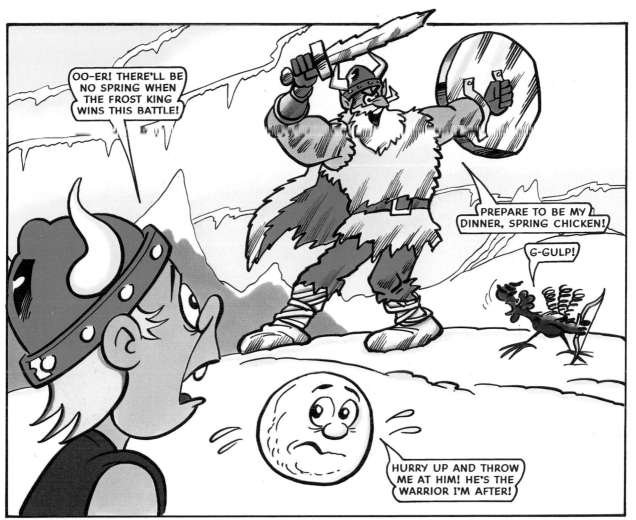

BEEZER BIRDS

WHATAHOOTUS BLINKUS

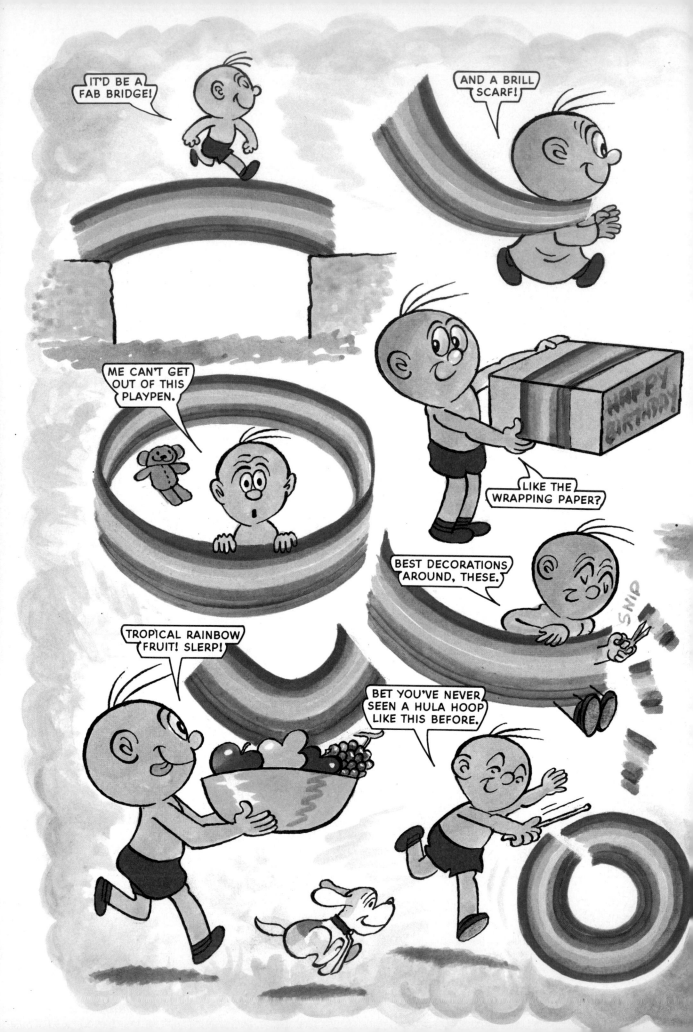

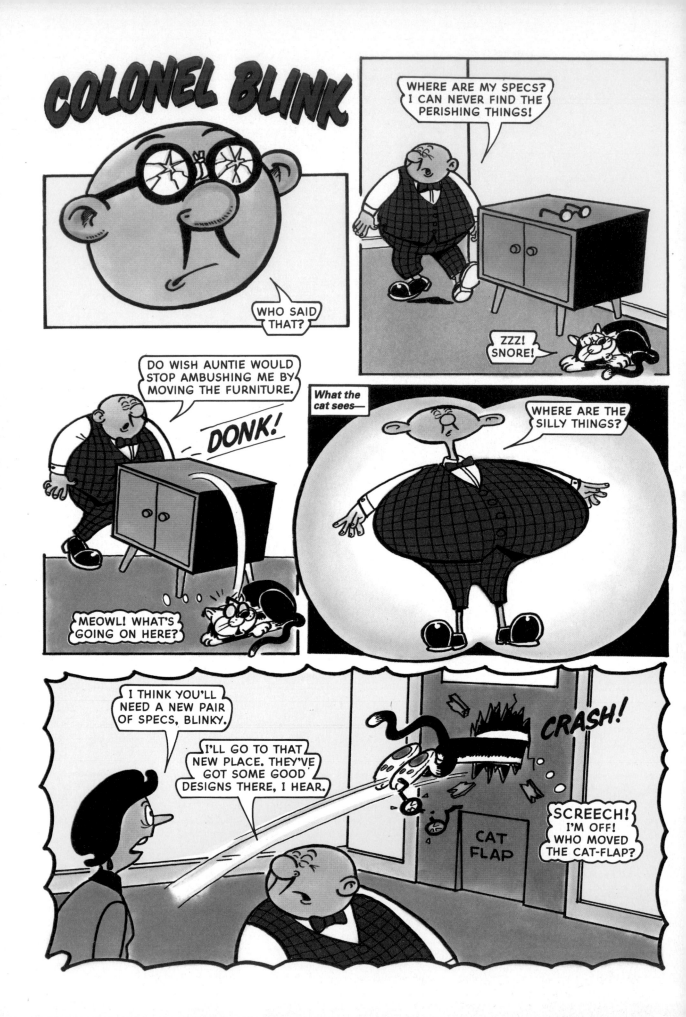

BEEZER BIRDS

BALDUS EAGLUS CROCKETTUS

The Banana Bunch

DOPEY'S TOUR DE FARCE!

JOIN The Bunch on Dopey's Tour de Farce! Use buttons for your bikes and throw a six to start. First to The Eiffel Tower wins. Bon Voyage!

Start

Chased by bull! Move on 3.

Braces caught on passing car! Move on 2.

Handlebars come off. Go back 2.

The Eiffel Tower. You've won!

Lips sore from blowing up flat tyre. Miss a turn.

"Service stop". Miss a turn.

Steep mountain. Slide back down 2.

Catch a lift. Zoom on 3.

Find your wheels are square. Miss a turn.

Over the top. Slide on 3.

BEEZER BIRDS

MAGPIO KNUCKUS
DAFTUS THEFTUS.

Then —

CAPTAIN ADRIAN and his BEEZER CREW

in THE ROUND THE UNIVERSE BOAT RACE

A FEATURE STORY STARRING YOUR **BEEZER** PALS

Minutes later —

GLUB! WHAT A PAIR OF HORRORS!

THIS WILL STOP YOUR WATERY TOMFOOLERY!

AW!

ROTTER!

MUST SHAKE MYSELF DRY!

ME TOO!

GROOH! I'M SOAKED!

LOOK AT THE MESS THE WATER'S MADE ON THAT WALL!

ULK!

GULP!

ON THE OTHER HAND, I'VE GOT ME AN IDEA!

LOVE THIS MODERN INTERIOR DECORATING! HAVE A FORTUNE!

THANKS! THE ANIMALS ARE BRILL AT THIS SORT OF THING!

BEEZER BIRDS

CUCKOO-US DOPEYUS MAXIMUS.

THE BADD LADS

Suddenly —

ROAR!

EEK! A G-G-G-G-G — APE!

Give me the moonlight! Give me the girl!

Ahem! Not quite what I'm after!

Well, hi, guys!

Ah! Mr Ostrich! How about you? Ever appeared in front of a camera?

Obviously not! Stop! Stop, old pal!

That's a microphone, not din-dins!

He's no use! What other animals are there?

Me lunch!

BEEZER BIRDS

MOSWANUS AND UGLYUS DUCKLINGUS MUGSYUS

JAB!

WELL, THAT'S IRONED OUT ANY WRINKLES I HAD, TOO!

NOW I'LL TAKE A NICE SHOWER!

AH! VERY REFRESHING! PITY IT'S NOT A BIT WARMER, THOUGH!

TRA-LA!

A QUICK RUB-DOWN AND I'M READY TO DO MY HAIR!

GOT TO HIT THIS HEDGE AT JUST THE RIGHT ANGLE!

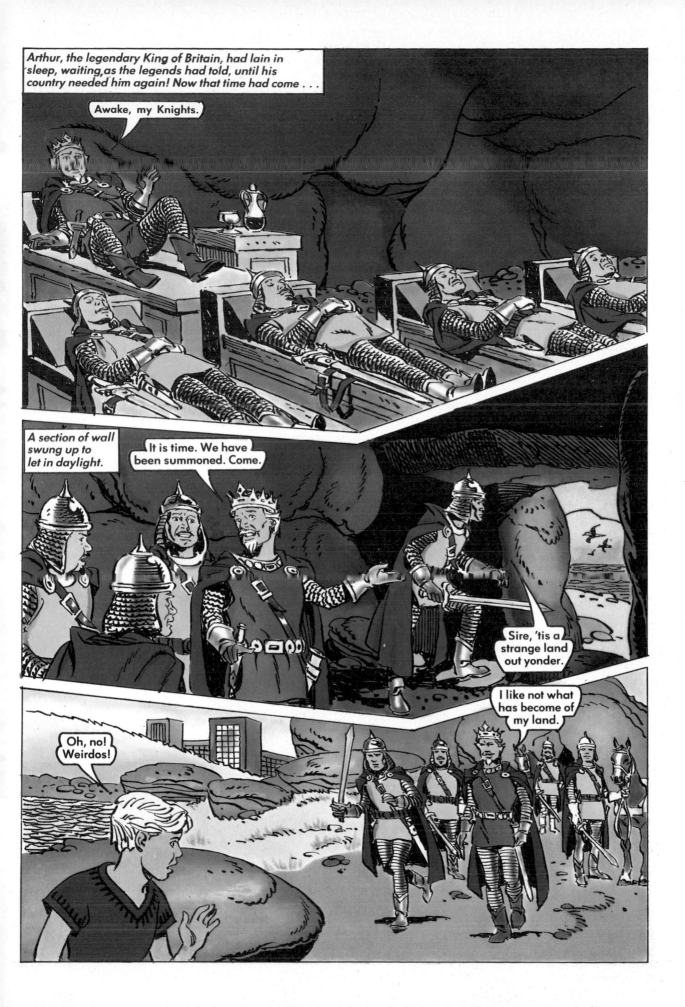

And—

SPLUTTER! I SHOULD HAVE KNOCKED THE SNOW OFF FIRST.

At last—
TIMBERR!

But then—

OOH! OW! IT'S TOO HEAVY!

TELL HIM TO LEAVE IT AND PICK A SMALLER ONE.

NONSENSE! I KNOW HOW TO GET IT HOME.

HE'LL FLY DOWN THE SLOPE IN SECONDS.

RIDE ON IT LIKE A SLEDGE

I DON'T LIKE THE SOUND OF THAT!

LITTLE MO

THAT'S ME!

OH-OH! HERE COMES MUGSY. I'LL BET HE'S OUT TO CAUSE TROUBLE!

STROLL

HELLO, MO, MY OLD PAL-TYPE CHUM AND BUDDY!

SLOPPY KISS!

UGH! GERROFF!

GONNA PLAY BAR FOOTBALL WITH ME, MO? HUH? PLEASE!

WELL, OKAY, BUT NO CHEATING!

I PROMISE!

A great big fib.

And so—

HERE WE GO! HERE WE GO! HERE WE GO!

BEEZER BIRDS

KINGFISHERUS
BARBARUS

PHOOT and MOUSE

N-N-NOW, LADIES! IT'S ONLY MY AFTERSHAVE!

HUH! NO **REAL** LION WOULD EVER GO IN THERE WITH ALL THOSE DOGS!

SKID!

SCREECH!

LEAP!

AFRICAN PLAIN DUST-BATH — RESERVED FOR VERY SMELLY HYENAS ONLY

THIS IS MY ONLY HOPE!

FURIOUS SCRUBBING OF LICE INFESTED ARMPITS!

SCRITCH! SCRATCH!

HORRENDOUS HUMMM!

CLAW!

PATENTED AUTOMATIC DE-PONGING INVENTION

Later —

ONCE I'VE GOT ALL THIS SMELLY STUFF OFF, I'VE GOT A FOOLPROOF PLAN TO SCARE PHOOT. JUST WATCH ME!

In Phoot's house —

HAR-DE-HAR-HAR! WHEN HE TAKES A HANKY, I'LL PUNCH 'IM RIGHT UP THE SCHNOZZ! WHAT A FRIGHT HE'LL GET!

JAB! JAB! HOOK! SWIPE!

BABY-BOT SOFT

HANDY HANKIES